CONSTELLATIONS

BY JAY CLARK

 GOLDEN PRESS · NEW YORK

CONTENTS

1969 Edition

© Copyright 1964, 1962, 1961, 1959, 1956, 1951 by Western
Publishing Company, Inc. Printed in the U.S.A.

CONSTELLATIONS are the patterns that people make from groups of stars in the sky. The Greeks and Romans named many of the constellations we know today after heroes, gods, and animals. Long ago people used the constellations as guides to the seasons and for planting crops. Constellations of the Zodiac (pp. 44-45) were believed to have mystical powers over human life. We use constellations as signposts to help locate stars and planets. In 1928, an international congress of astronomers set the boundaries of the 88 constellations that have been named.

Saturn moves through 4 constellations during a 10-year period.

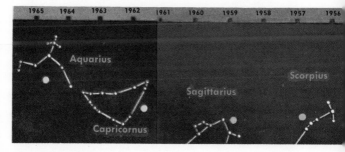

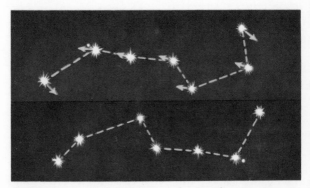

Big Dipper now (top) with arrows showing direction stars are moving; (bottom) as it will appear in the year 100,000.

STARS, which make up the constellations, are balls of glowing gas. Their light is caused by nuclear reactions. Their colors vary from cool red (5500 degrees F.) to hot blue-white (55,000 degrees F.). The nearest star to us is the sun. The distances of stars are so great that they are measured in light years—a light year being the distance light travels in one year at a speed of 186,000 miles per second. Stars move at speeds of many miles per second. They move at different speeds and in different directions, so the pattern of every constellation gradually changes.

4

MAGNITUDE, the brightness of a star as seen from the earth, depends on the star's distance and on the amount of light the star actually sends out. A first-magnitude star is 2½ times brighter than a second-magnitude star, and a second-magnitude star is 2½ times brighter than one of third magnitude, and so on. A star brighter than first magnitude is of zero or minus magnitude. The sun's magnitude is −27. A sixth-magnitude star is the faintest that the eye can see without a telescope.

THE BRIGHTEST STARS

Name	Constellation	Magnitude	Name	Constellation	Magnitude
Sirius	Canis Major	−1.4	Achernar	Eridanus	+0.5
Canopus	Carina	−0.7	Beta Centauri	Centaurus	+0.7
Alpha Centauri	Centaurus	−0.3	Betelgeuse	Orion	+0.7
Arcturus	Boötes	−0.1	Altair	Aquila	+0.8
Vega	Lyra	0.0	Aldebaran	Taurus	+0.8
Capella	Auriga	+0.1	Alpha Crucis	Crux	+0.9
Rigel	Orion	+0.2	Antares	Scorpius	+1.0
Procyon	Canis Minor	+0.4	Spica	Virgo	+1.0

MOVEMENTS OF STARS AND CONSTEL-LATIONS, as we see them, are partly due to the earth's movements. Because the earth rotates daily on its axis, the stars appear to revolve around it daily, rising in the east. The earth also revolves around the sun once a year, so there is an extra revolution of the stars spread out over the year. Stars rise and set four minutes earlier

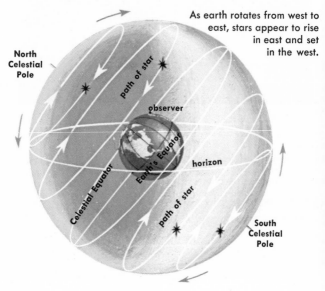

As earth rotates from west to east, stars appear to rise in east and set in the west.

North Celestial Pole

path of star

observer

Celestial Equator

Earth's Equator

horizon

path of star

South Celestial Pole

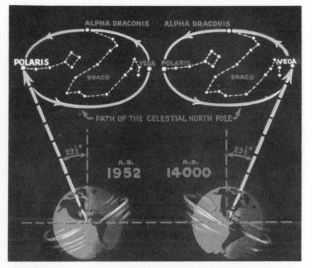

The direction of the earth's axis changes slowly, so that the North Pole traces a circular path in the sky.

each day (two hours earlier each month), so the constellations that are visible change with the seasons. Finally, the earth wobbles on its axis because of the pull of the moon. This movement, called precession, completed each 26,000 years, makes the North Pole trace a circle in the sky, pointing to different stars as the "north star."

7

**CIRCUMPOLAR CONSTEL-
LATIONS** To an observer at
either the North or the South
Pole, the northern or southern
constellations never rise or set
but can be seen all night, circling
slowly. At the equator, all constellations appear to rise and set.
The farther north or south of the
equator you are, the more northern or southern constellations
you see that do not rise and set.
These constellations are called
circumpolar. The five constellations shown here and on the following pages are circumpolar at
the latitude of Chicago, New
York, Rome, and farther north.

To see how these constellations
appear about 9 p.m. during any
particular month, rotate the chart
so that the name of that month is
at the top.

8

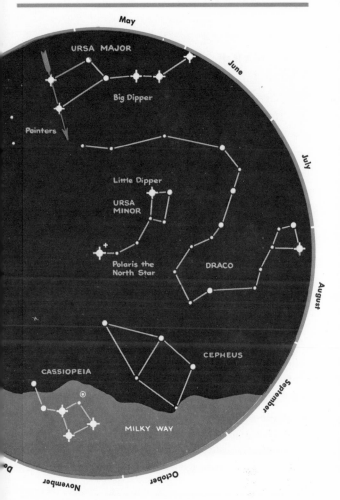

URSA MAJOR, the Great Bear, is the easiest constellation to find in the Northern Hemisphere because the Big Dipper is an important part of it. The three stars that form the Big Dipper's handle are also the Great Bear's tail. The rest of the bear extends in front and below the Dipper's bowl. Early in an autumn evening, Ursa Major is low in the sky. In winter, it rises higher and by spring is high in the north. By summer, it starts descending.

URSA MINOR, the Little Bear or Little Dipper, has seven stars. At the end of its handle is Polaris, the North Star. At the equator, Polaris is seen on the horizon; at the North Pole, directly over-head. At latitudes in between, the height of Polaris (in degrees) is the same as the observer's latitude. The four stars in the bowl are of second, third, fourth, and fifth magnitude. Magnitudes of other stars can be estimated by comparing them to these stars.

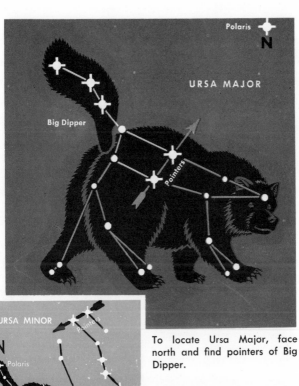

To locate Ursa Major, face north and find pointers of Big Dipper.

To find Ursa Minor, find Polaris by means of pointers. Then follow handle to bowl of dipper.

11

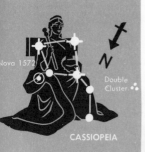

CASSIOPEIA

Cassiopeia is opposite the Big Dipper, on the other side of Polaris, and about the same distance away. The pointers aim toward it.

Cepheus is between Cassiopeia and Draco. Follow a line from the pointers of the Big Dipper through Polaris to the star that makes the peak of the roof.

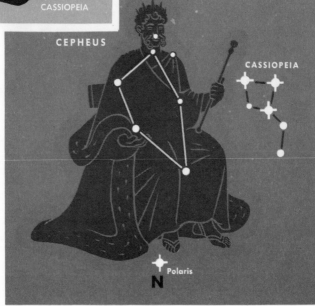

CEPHEUS

CASSIOPEIA

Polaris
N

12

CASSIOPEIA is shaped like the letter **M** when it is above the Pole Star, and like a **W** when it is below. Five main stars form the constellation. The brightest nova (exploding star) ever seen appeared near Cassiopeia in 1572. This super-nova was visible, even in daytime, for more than a year before it faded. Cassiopeia is overhead in fall and continues around the sky with the pass-ing seasons. Cassiopeia was an ancient queen of Ethiopia.

CEPHEUS is a constellation of five stars shaped like a small house with a steep roof. The star at the peak of the roof is always closest to Polaris. The most important star in Cepheus is the one farthest from Polaris, for it is the brightest of the class of stars called Cepheid variables. These stars, which change regularly in brightness, are used to measure distances of star clusters and galaxies. King Cepheus was Cassiopeia's hus-band.

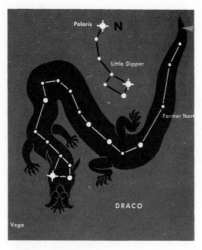

The four stars forming the head of Draco can be located along a line extending from the bowl of the Little Dipper to Vega, in the constellation Lyra.

DRACO, the Dragon, is not easy to distinguish, for its stars are faint and its twisting shape is difficult to follow. The best time to view Draco is in late spring or early summer, when it is highest in the sky. Thuban, the third star from the end of the tail, is the most famous star of Draco. About 5,000 years ago Thuban, not Polaris, was the North Star. Draco winds between the two dippers, and its tail ends not far from the Big Dipper's pointers.

Meteor trail in a spring sky.

SPRING is an excellent time to view the stars. Eleven first-magnitude stars are visible, more than at any other time of the year. About April 20, meteor showers can be seen coming from Lyra, a constellation that is more easily seen in summer (page 24).

The constellation Leo is at the center of the spring sky. Boötes and Virgo are also seen. Boötes is the hero of two legends. In one he is a herdsman hunting the Big Bear, Ursa Major. In the other he uses the Big Dipper as a plow to make a furrow across the sky.

15

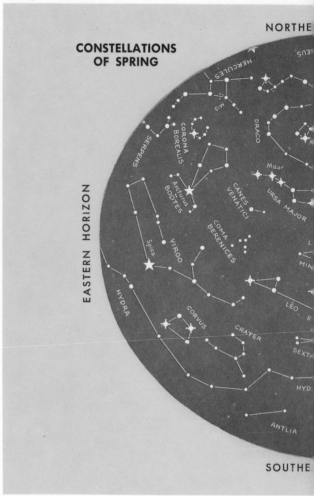

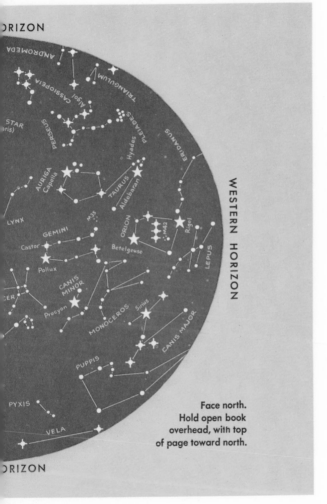

Face north.
Hold open book
overhead, with top
of page toward north.

Arcturus is the key to finding Boötes. Continue the curve of the Big Dipper's handle to the orange star.

Find Leo by following a line from the pointers of the Big Dipper in the direction away from Polaris.

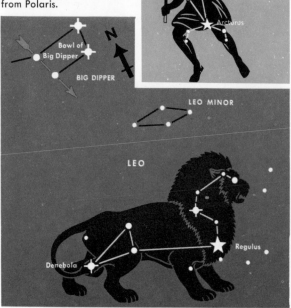

18

BOÖTES, the Herdsman, is a kite-shaped constellation near the end of the Big Dipper's handle. At the base of the kite is an orange star, Arcturus, the brightest in the constellation. It is about 24 times larger and 83 times brighter than our sun. Light from Arcturus was used to open the Chicago Century of Progress Fair in 1933. The light used took 40 years to reach the earth. When the light left Arcturus, the World's Fair of 1893 had just opened in Chicago.

LEO, the Lion, is the most important spring constellation. Leo is made of two separate sections. The head and front, formed of six stars, are in the shape of a sickle. Regulus, at the base of the sickle, is a first-magnitude double star (two stars that appear so close together that we ordinarily see them as one). Each November, meteors called Leonids appear near the sickle of Leo. The second, smaller part of Leo is the triangular tail section.

VIRGO, the Virgin, is another large spring constellation. It covers a great area of the sky and can be divided into two sections. The easiest part to recognize is shaped roughly like the letter **Y.** Spica, a white first-magnitude star 230 light years from the earth, is at the bottom of the stem of the **Y.** The other stars are third and fourth magnitude. The second part of Virgo consists of

two roughly parallel lines of three stars each. Spica is at the end of the southern line. The region near Virgo is noted for its cluster of several hundred galaxies.

Continue the curve of the Big Dipper's handle through Arcturus, about an equal distance, to locate the bright, white Spica.

SUMMER skies have fewer bright stars but more constellations than do the skies of spring. The Milky Way is especially clear at this time of year, being brightest in the constellation Sagittarius. In summer the triangle of Deneb, Vega, and Altair dominates the sky. The Northern Cross (Cygnus), with Deneb marking its top, is located in this triangle (pages 22 and 28).

A dense portion of the Milky Way in the summer sky.

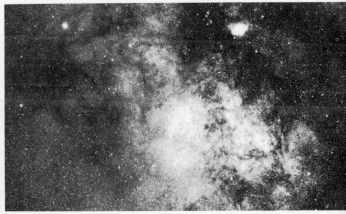

Summer Constellations

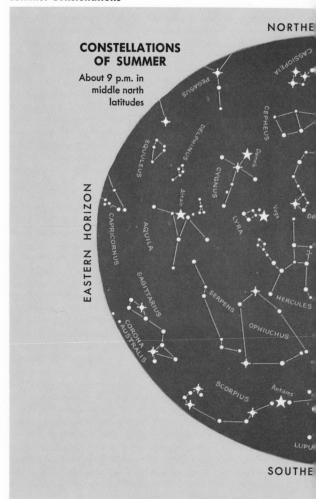

CONSTELLATIONS
OF SUMMER

About 9 p.m. in
middle north
latitudes

NORTHE

EASTERN HORIZON

SOUTHE

22

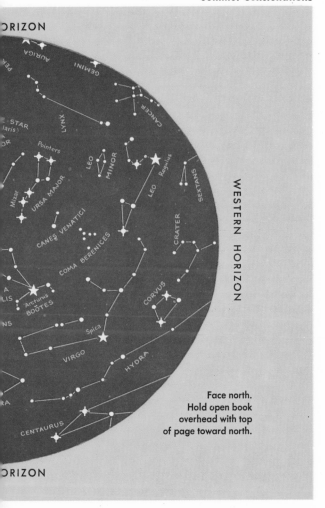

Face north.
Hold open book
overhead with top
of page toward north.

LYRA, the Lyre or Harp, is a small constellation that contains a blue-white star, Vega, the brightest star of summer. Vega is 26 light years away. About 14,000 years ago, it was the North Star, and in the future it will become the North Star again (page 7). Vega can be seen the year round from the United States northward.

The other five stars in Lyra are of third and fourth magnitude.

SCORPIUS, the Scorpion, is visible for only a month or so during the year in northern United States. Then it appears low on the southern horizon. To the south it is visible longer and appears higher above the horizon. Its head points to the west; its tail, to the east.

Scorpius contains the giant first-magnitude star Antares. This huge red double star has a diameter 330 times greater than our sun's and is 400 light years away.

Locate Vega by following a line from the back two stars of the Big Dipper's bowl through the second-magnitude star in the head of Draco.

Scorpius appears low in the southern sky on a line from the head of Draco through Hercules.

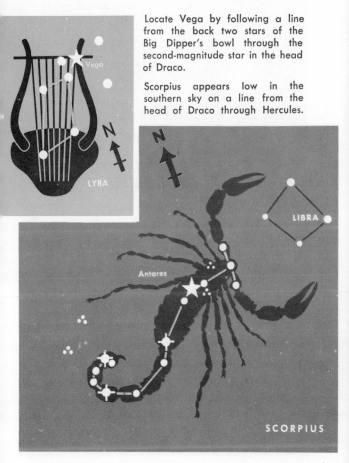

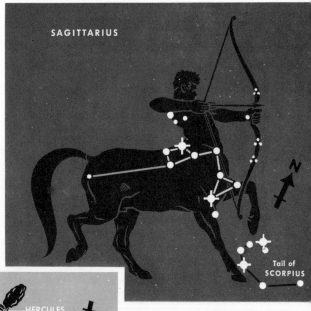

Sagittarius is located to the east and a little north of Scorpius, in the southern sky in summer.

In midsummer, Hercules is almost overhead, just south of the head of Draco, between Vega and Arcturus.

SAGITTARIUS, the Archer, is found deep in the Milky Way. The constellation's two brightest stars are of second magnitude. Its shape is an upside-down, six-star dipper with its handle pointing west into the thickest part of the Milky Way. At the end of the dipper's handle is a small triangle of stars. The triangle and bowl of the dipper each contain one of the two second-magnitude stars. The Milk Dipper of Sagittarius is the easiest part to identify.

HERCULES, the Kneeling Man, has no first- or second-magnitude stars. The figure appears upside down, so that, unlike most constellations, the head is to the south. The middle section of Hercules is a rough square. On the western side and along its outer edge is M 13, the Great Cluster. This cluster of more than 100,000 stars, over 30,000 light years from the earth, is a faint fuzzy spot to the unaided eye. Viewed through a telescope, it is a spray of glimmering points of light.

CYGNUS, the Swan, is perhaps better known as the Northern Cross (page 21). Cygnus is in the brightest part of the Milky Way, at the point where it divides. The bright star at the top of the cross is the first-magnitude star Deneb, about 650 light years away.

AQUILA, the Eagle, just south of Cygnus, is marked by the first-magnitude star Altair in the center of a short line of three stars. The blue-white Altair is 16 light years away.

Cygnus is east of the constellation Lyra. To its south is Aquila, with Sagitta and Delphinus between them.

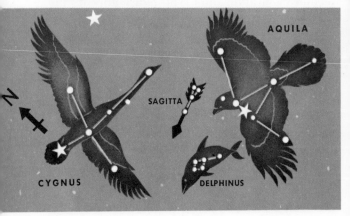

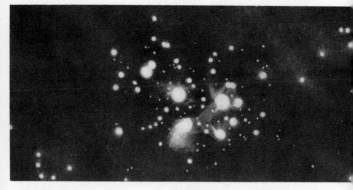

The Pleiades are worth seeing through binoculars in late autumn.

AUTUMN skies contain only a few bright stars. The constellations are close together and difficult to distinguish. Some of the summer constellations are still visible in the west. One of the interesting stars of autumn is <u>Mira</u>, a variable star in the constellation Cetus. Over a period of about ten months Mira's brightness varies from second to seventh magnitude as it dims and brightens again. A cluster of gems in the late autumn sky is the Pleiades, a small dipper-like constellation close to Perseus. The Pleiades are actually a part of Taurus (page 41).

29

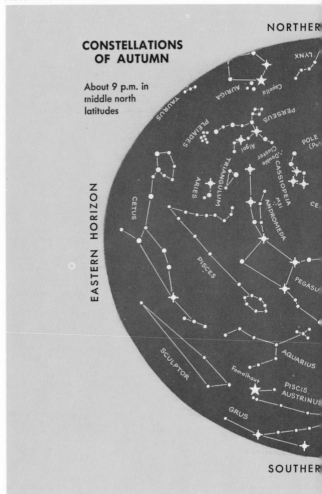

CONSTELLATIONS OF AUTUMN

About 9 p.m. in middle north latitudes

NORTHER

EASTERN HORIZON

SOUTHER

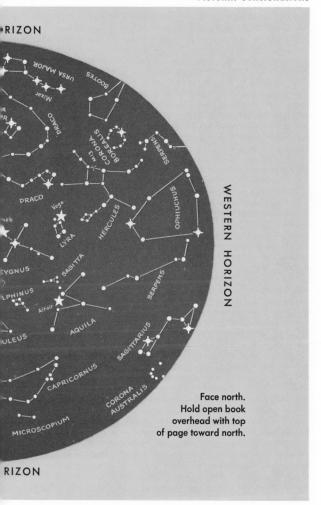

Face north.
Hold open book
overhead with top
of page toward north.

31

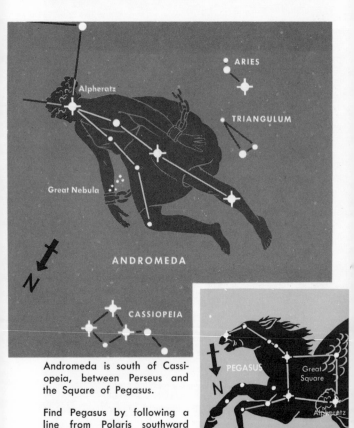

Andromeda is south of Cassiopeia, between Perseus and the Square of Pegasus.

Find Pegasus by following a line from Polaris southward through the western side of Cassiopeia.

ANDROMEDA is an unusual constellation because Alpheratz, a triple star, joins it to Pegasus, the next constellation. Each line making the long V of Andromeda consists of three stars. The longer southern line contains two second-magnitude stars. North of Andromeda and just visible is M 31, a large bright spiral galaxy 2 million light years away, made up of almost two hundred billion stars. In the Northern Hemisphere, it is the galaxy nearest to our own that is visible.

PEGASUS, the Winged Horse, is the first of the autumn constellations to appear in the east. Its main part is a large, uneven square formed by four stars. One of the four, Alpheratz, is also part of Andromeda. Three of the four stars forming the square are of second magnitude. Pegasus, like Andromeda and Hercules, appears upside down, its head toward the south. The square of Pegasus appears to be quite empty, but in large telescopes many stars can be seen there.

TRIANGULUM, the Triangle, is east of Andromeda. Its brightest star is of third magnitude. Triangulum is a triangle, small but very clear. In it is M 33, a spiral galaxy. Look for it with binoculars.

ARIES, the Ram, is located southeast of Triangulum. It also forms a triangle, though not as distinct. Its three main stars are of second, third, and fourth magnitude.

Aries is south and slightly east of Triangulum and north of Pisces.

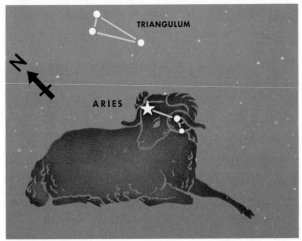

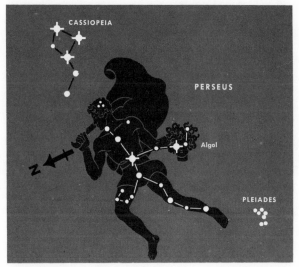

Perseus is south of Cassiopeia and east of Andromeda, between Polaris and the Pleiades.

PERSEUS resembles a running letter **K**. The constellation's two brightest stars are second magnitude. One of these is the famous double variable star, Algol. Its brightness dims about every three days when the larger and fainter of the two stars passes between the earth and the smaller, brighter star.

35

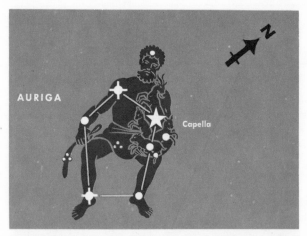

Follow a line forward through the two stars forming the top of the Big Dipper's dipper to Auriga and its bright star, Capella.

AURIGA, the Charioteer, might just as well be considered a winter constellation. It is a kite-shaped group of first-, second-, and third-magnitude stars, including Capella, the sixth brightest star. Capella is a triple star 45 light years away and 16 times the diameter of the sun. Auriga has several star clusters, each composed of about one hundred stars and each about 2,700 light years away.

36

The Great Nebula of Orion shows glowing gases in this telescopic photograph.

WINTER is the most exciting time to study the stars and constellations. No other season offers such a clear view of the heavens, and even the faintest stars seem to shine more brightly. Eight first-magnitude stars can be seen in the winter sky. Nights are longer, so you have more time to observe.

Orion, the most distinctive winter constellation, can be used as an aid to find all others.

37

CONSTELLATIONS OF WINTER

About 9 p.m. in middle north latitudes

NORTHER

EASTERN HORIZON

SOUTHER

38

Face north.
Hold open book
overhead with top
of page toward north.

Orion cannot be missed. To check, follow a line from Polaris, southward through Capella in Auriga, to Orion.

ORION, the Hunter, is the brightest constellation. The main part is five-sided. Betelgeuse, in the northeast corner, is a giant red star 190 light years away. Rigel, at the southwest corner, is a blue-white star about 540 light years away. The belt of Orion has three stars in a short, slanting row from which hangs the sword containing the Great Nebula, M 42.

TAURUS, the Bull, is composed of seven stars and looks like a long letter **V**. Four of the five stars nearest the angle of the **V** belong to the Hyades cluster. Aldebaran, the fifth star near the angle, is a red, double, first-magnitude star about 75 light years closer than the others. To the west is another cluster, the Pleiades. Only six to twelve of the 250 stars in it can be seen without a telescope.

Taurus is southwest of Auriga and northwest of Orion. One star of Taurus is also a star in Auriga.

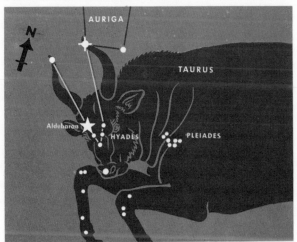

41

CANIS MAJOR, the Big Dog, contains Sirius, the brightest star in the sky. Sirius, a blue-white double star of first magnitude, is one of the nearest stars to the earth, just 8.6 light years away. Four other stars in Canis Major are second magnitude. Below Sirius you can see a cluster of stars, M 41, without a telescope.

CANIS MINOR, the Little Dog, is a very small constellation of only two visible stars. Procyon, the brighter of the two, is a double star of first magnitude.

GEMINI, the Twins, is like a large letter **U.** The constellation's two main stars are Pollux and Castor. Pollux, the southernmost of the two, is a yellow star about 32 light years away. Five other stars extend in a line from Pollux to Orion. Castor, a white second-magnitude star, is 45 light years away. A line of five stars also extends toward Orion.

The belt of Orion points southeast to Sirius in Canis Major.

Procyon is the first bright star due south of Castor and Pollux.

A line north from Rigel through Betelgeuse in Orion points to Pollux in Gemini.

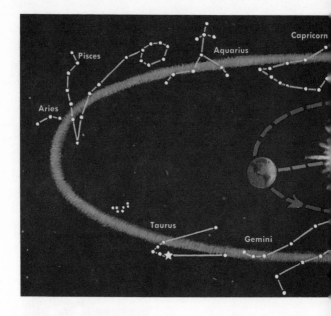

ZODIAC is a Greek word meaning "circle of animals." It is a group of twelve constellations forming the apparent pathway of the sun around the earth. The moon and the nine planets also follow this path. Aries, the Ram; Taurus, the Bull; Cancer, the Crab; Leo, the Lion; Scorpius, the Scorpion; Capricornus, the Sea Goat; and

44

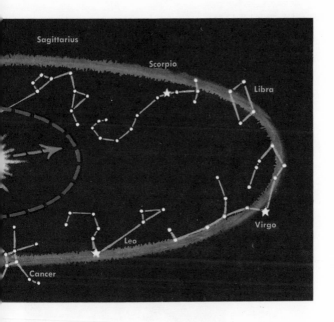

Pisces, the Fishes—these seven are the constellations named for animals by the Greeks. The other five are: Virgo, the Virgin; Sagittarius, the Archer; Gemini, the Twins; Libra, the Balance; and Aquarius, the Water Bearer.

The Zodiac constellations are useful in locating planets.

TELLING TIME   Consider Polaris as the center of a clock (to which the hands would be attached). Let the two pointer stars of the Big Dipper be the hour hand. During a 12-hour period, the pointers will move almost exactly 180 degrees, or halfway around Polaris. In six hours they will move 90 degrees, or a quarter swing. Thus by dividing the sky around Polaris into quarters, you can judge the passage of time.

Polaris is at the center of the sky clock, with the Big Dipper's pointer stars forming its hour hand.

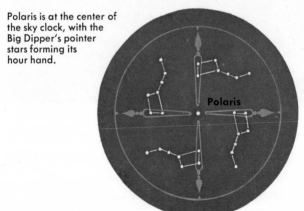

QUIZ-ME

Here are some questions you can answer if you have read this book. The pages where the answers will be found are listed at the end.

1 What is the nearest star to the earth?
2 In what constellation is the nearest spiral galaxy seen?
3 Do north circumpolar constellations ever appear to rise or set in the Northern Hemisphere?
4 How many constellations are recognized by astronomers?
5 Name the kite-shaped constellation near the Big Dipper's handle.
6 At the North Pole, where does one see the pole star?
7 Which two major constellations share some of the same stars?
8 Name the north circumpolar constellation shaped like a small house with a steep roof.

9 Light from what star was used to open the Century of Progess Fair in Chicago?

10 How many constellations are there in the Zodiac?

11 Which is the brightest constellation of winter?

12 What is the brightest star of summer?

13 Why do stars seem to rise in the east?

14 What spring constellation has a sickle-shaped head?

15 What is the popular name for Cygnus, the Swan?

16 What is the brightest star in the sky?

17 What famous star of Draco was once the North Star?

ANSWERS: 1 (p. 4), **2** (p. 33), **3** (p. 8), **4** (p. 3), **5** (p. 19), **6** (p. 10), **7** (p. 33), **8** (p. 13), **9** (p. 19), **10** (p. 44), **11** (p. 40), **12** (p. 24), **13** (p. 6), **14** (p. 19), **15** (p. 28), **16** (p. 42), **17** (p. 14).

ILLUSTRATIONS BY: *Nino Carbe, James Gordon Irving, Ken Martin*

COVER BY: *George Solonevich*

PHOTOS: *p. 21 Yerkes; p. 37 Clarence P. Custer, M.D.*